Ballads Of The 90s

This publication is not authorised for sale in the United States of America and/or Canada.

Wise Publications
London/New York/Paris/Sydney/Copenhagen/Madrid/Tokyo

Exclusive Distributors:
Music Sales Limited
8/9 Frith Street, London W1D 3JB, England.
Music Sales Pty Limited
120 Rothschild Avenue, Rosebery, NSW 2018, Australia.

Order No. AM970563
ISBN 0-7119-8883-8
This book © Copyright 2001 by Wise Publications

Unauthorised reproduction of any part of this publication by any means including photocopying is an
infringement of copyright.

Compiled by Nick Crispin
Music arranged by Stephen Duro
Music processed by Allegro Reproductions
Cover photograph (Robbie Williams) courtesy of LFI

Printed in the United Kingdom by
Printwise (Haverhill) Limited, Suffolk

Your Guarantee of Quality
As publishers, we strive to produce every book to the highest commercial standards.
This book has been carefully designed to minimise awkward page turns and to make
playing from it a real pleasure.
Particular care has been given to specifying acid-free, neutral-sized paper made from pulps
which have not been elemental chlorine bleached. This pulp is from farmed sustainable forests
and was produced with special regard for the environment.
Throughout, the printing and binding have been planned to ensure a sturdy, attractive publication
which should give years of enjoyment.
If your copy fails to meet our high standards, please inform us and we will gladly replace it.

Music Sales' complete catalogue describes thousands of titles and is available in full colour sections
by subject, direct from Music Sales Limited. Please state your areas of interest
and send a cheque/postal order for £1.50 for postage to:
Music Sales Limited, Newmarket Road, Bury St. Edmunds, Suffolk IP33 3YB.

www.musicsales.com

(Everything I Do) I Do It For You

Words by Bryan Adams & Robert John Lange
Music by Michael Kamen

© Copyright 1991 Miracle Creek Music Incorporated & Zachary Creek Music Incorporated, administered by Universal/
MCA Music Limited, 77 Fulham Palace Road, London W6 (62.5%)/2855 Music & Almo Music Corporation,
administered by Rondor Music (London) Limited, 10a Parsons Green, London SW6 (18.75%)/
Out Of Pocket Productions Limited, administered by Zomba Music Publishers Limited, 165-167 High Road, London NW10 (18.75%).
All Rights Reserved. International Copyright Secured.

2. Look into your heart
   You will find there's nothin' there to hide
   Take me as I am, take my life
   I would give it all, I would sacrifice.

   Don't tell me it's not worth fightin' for
   I can't help it, there's nothin' I want more
   You know it's true, everything I do
   I do it for you.

Love Is All Around

Words & Music by Reg Presley

© Copyright 1967 Dick James Music Limited.
Universal/Dick James Music Limited, 77 Fulham Palace Road, London W6.
All Rights Reserved. International Copyright Secured.

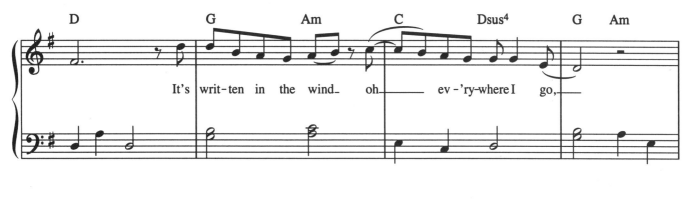

It's writ-ten in the wind oh ev-'ry-where I go,

So if you real-ly love me, come on and let it

show. Come on and let it, come on and let it,

come on and let it, come on and let it show.

Verse 2:

I see your face before me
As I lay on my bed;
I cannot get to thinking
Of all the things you said.
You gave your promise to me
And I gave mine to you;
I need someone beside me
In everything I do.

More Than Words

Words & Music by Nuno Bettencourt & Gary Cherone

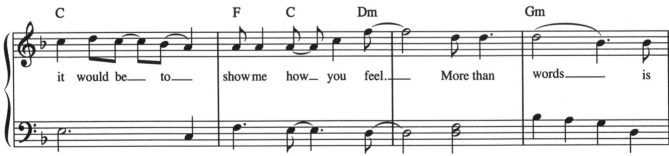

© Copyright 1990 Almo Music Corporation/Color Me Blind Music, USA.
Rondor Music (London) Limited, 10a Parsons Green, London SW6 for the United Kingdom,
the Republic of Ireland and PRS Territories (except Hong Kong, Malaysia & Singapore).
All Rights Reserved. International Copyright Secured.

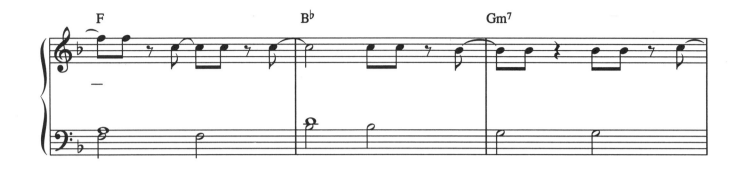

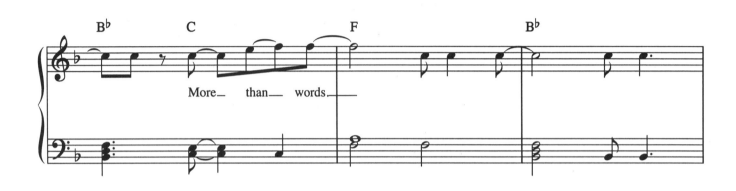

More— than— words—

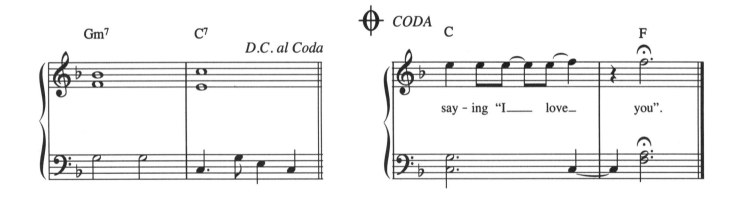

D.C. al Coda

CODA

say - ing "I— love— you".

Verse 2:

Now that I've tried to talk to you
And make you understand
All you have to do is close your eyes
And just reach out your hands
And touch me
Hold me close, don't ever let me go
More than words
Is all I ever needed you to show
Then you wouldn't have to say
That you love me
'Cause I'd already know.

No Matter What

Music by Andrew Lloyd Webber
Words by Jim Steinman

Moderately

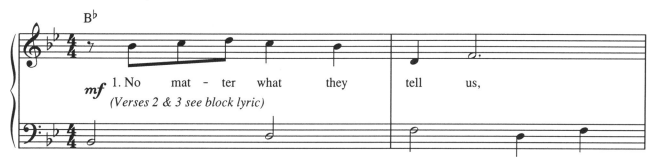

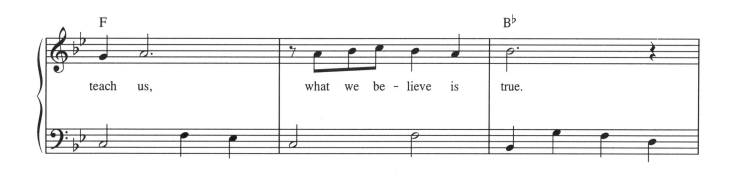

© Copyright 1998 The Really Useful Group Limited (50%)/Lost Boys Music/
Universal Music Publishing Limited, 77 Fulham Palace Road, London W6 (50%).
All Rights Reserved. International Copyright Secured.

-tack, no mat - ter where they take us,

we'll find our own way back. I can't de - ny___ what

I be - lieve,___ I can't be___ what I'm not.___

1, 2.

I know our love's for - ev - er, I know no mat - ter

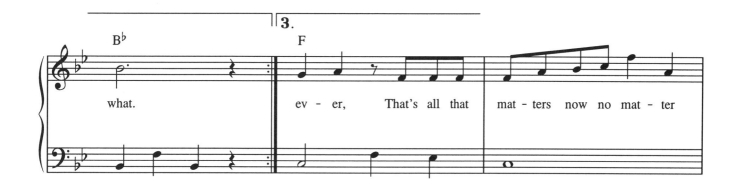

what.   ev - er,   That's all that   mat - ters now no mat - ter

what.   I know no mat - ter   what.

Verse 2:

If only tears were laughter,
If only night was day,
If only prayers were answered
Then we would hear God say.
No matter what they tell us,
No matter what they do,
No matter what they teach you,
What you believe is true.
And I will keep you safe and strong
And sheltered from the storm.
No matter where it's barren
Our dream is being born.

Verse 3:
Instrumental:

No matter if the sun don't shine,
Or if the skies are blue.
No matter what the ending,
My life began with you.
I can't deny what I believe,
I can't be what I'm not.
I know this love's for ever,
That's all that matters now no matter what.

Perfect Moment

Words & Music by James Marr & Wendy Page

Moderately

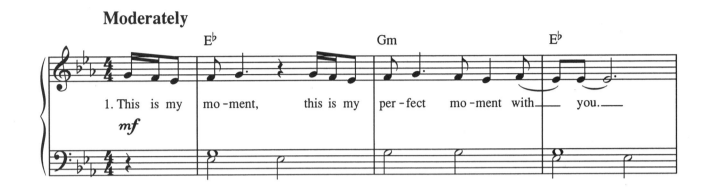

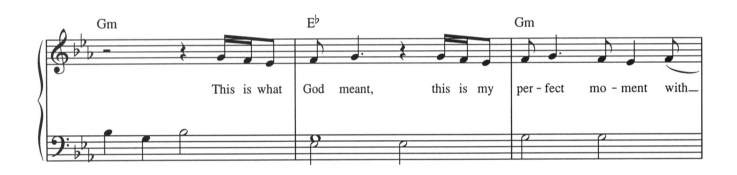

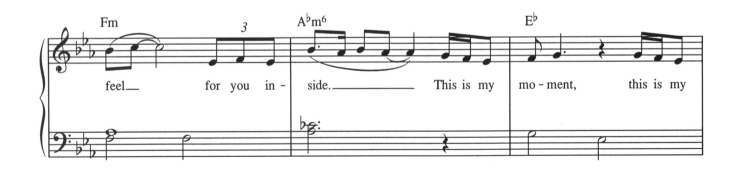

© Copyright 1999 Chrysalis Music Limited, The Chrysalis Building, 13 Bramley Road, London W10.
All Rights Reserved. International Copyright Secured.

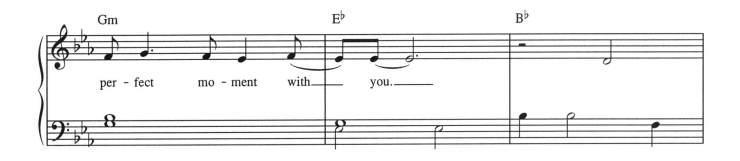

per - fect mo - ment with____ you.____

2. Tell me you love me when you__ leave. You're more than a sha -dow,

that's what I____ be -lieve. You take me to pla-ces I ne-ver thought I'd see.____

Min - ute by min -ute you're the world to me.__ I wish I could frame____ the look in your

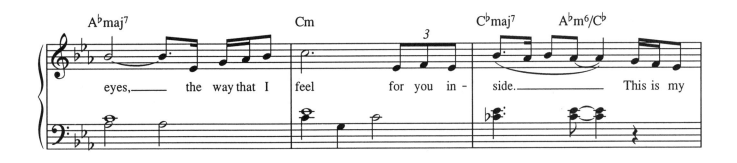

eyes,____ the way that I feel for you in- side.____ This is my

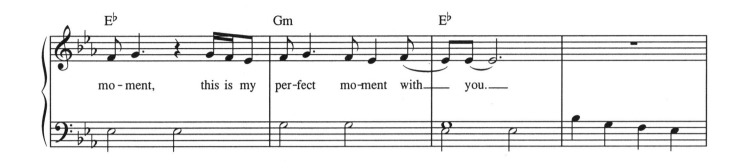

mo-ment, this is my per-fect mo-ment with you.

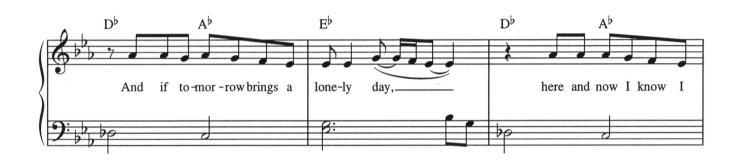

And if to-mor-row brings a lone-ly day, here and now I know I

have-n't lived in vain. No more tears in the rain, and if love ne-ver comes a-gain I can

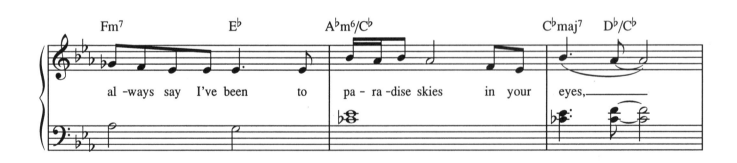

al-ways say I've been to pa-ra-dise skies in your eyes,

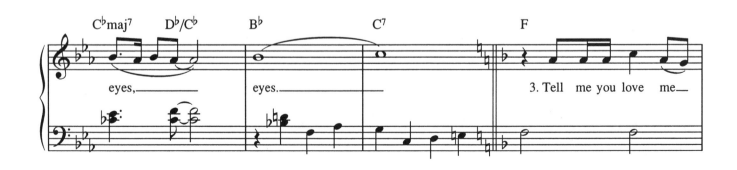

eyes, eyes. 3. Tell me you love me

18

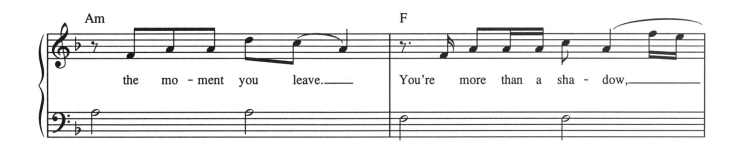

the mo - ment you leave._____ You're more than a sha - dow,_____

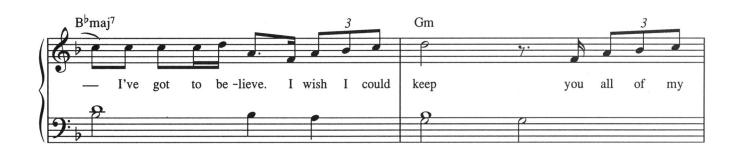

_____ I've got to be -lieve. I wish I could keep you all of my

life,_____ the way that I feel_____ for you__ in - side._____ This is my

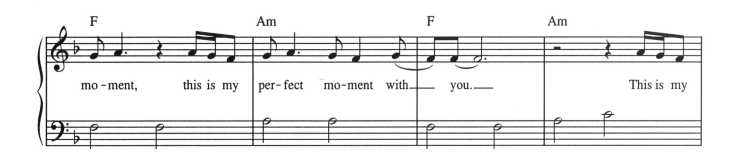

mo - ment, this is my per - fect mo - ment with__ you.__ This is my

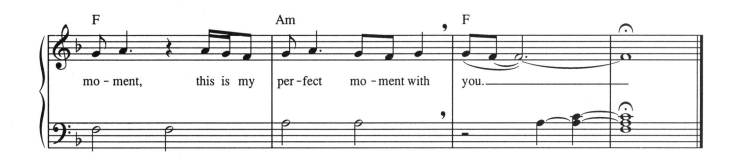

mo - ment, this is my per - fect mo - ment with you._____

Runaway

Words & Music by Andrea Corr, Caroline Corr, Sharon Corr & Jim Corr

© Copyright 1995 Universal-Songs Of PolyGram International Incorporated/Beacon Communications Music Company, USA.
Universal Music Publishing Limited, 77 Fulham Palace Road, London W6.
All Rights Reserved. International Copyright Secured.

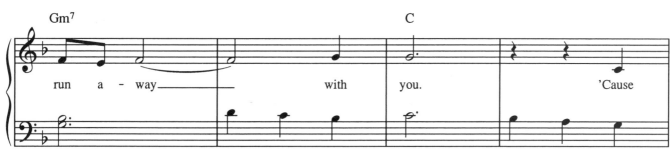

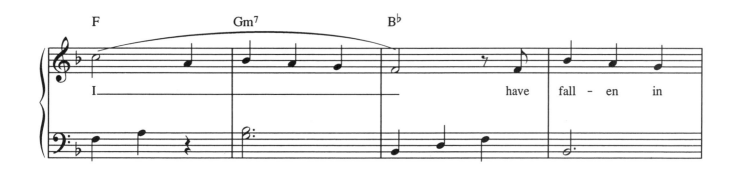

you.

D.S. al Coda

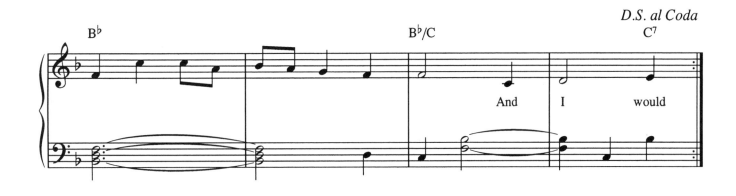

And   I   would

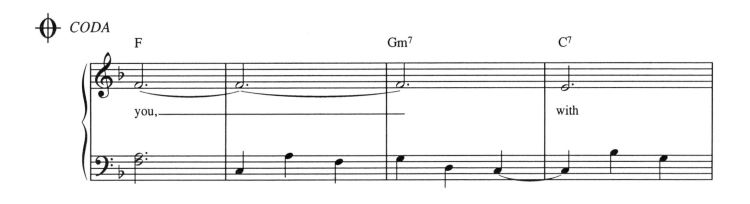

CODA

you,____   with

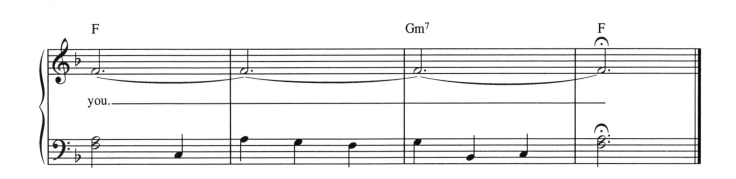

you.____

Stay Another Day

Words & Music by Tony Mortimer, Robert Kean & Dominic Hawken

Ba - by if you've got to go a - way, don't think I can take the pain, won't you stay a - no - ther day.

© Copyright 1994 Porky Publishing/Bandmodel Limited.
Universal Music Publishing Limited, 77 Fulham Palace Road, London W6.
All Rights Reserved. International Copyright Secured.

From: *"Richard Marx Greatest Hits"*

Right Here Waiting

by

RICHARD MARX

Published Under License From

WARNER BROS. PUBLICATIONS, INC.

© 1989 CHI-BOY MUSIC (ASCAP)
Rights for CHI-BOY MUSIC outside North America Administered by WB MUSIC CORP.
All Rights Reserved

Available at musicnotes.com
search for: MN0015896

NOTICE: Purchasers of this musical file are entitled to use it for their personal enjoyment and musical fulfillment. However, any duplication, adaptation, arranging and/or transmission of this copyrighted music requires the written consent of the copyright owner(s) and of WARNER BROS. PUBLICATIONS, INC. Unauthorized uses are infringements of the copyright laws of the United States and other countries and may subject the user to civil and/or criminal penalties.

𝄞 musicnotes.com

RIGHT HERE WAITING

Words and Music by
RICHARD MARX

Am

Verse:

Csus2

Csus2/F

From: "Richard Marx Greatest Hits"

Right Here Waiting

by

RICHARD MARX

Published Under License From

WARNER BROS. PUBLICATIONS, INC.

© 1989 CHI-BOY MUSIC (ASCAP)
Rights for CHI-BOY MUSIC outside North America Administered by WB MUSIC CORP.
All Rights Reserved

Available at **musicnotes.com**
search for: **MN0015896**

NOTICE: Purchasers of this musical file are entitled to use it for their personal enjoyment and musical fulfillment. However, any duplication, adaptation, arranging and/or transmission of this copyrighted music requires the written consent of the copyright owner(s) and of WARNER BROS. PUBLICATIONS, INC. Unauthorized uses are infringements of the copyright laws of the United States and other countries and may subject the user to civil and/or criminal penalties.

 musicnotes.com

Verse 2:

I touch your face while you are sleeping
And hold your hand
Don't understand what's going on
Good times we had return to haunt me
Though it's for you
All that I do seems to be wrong.

She's The One

Words & Music by Karl Wallinger

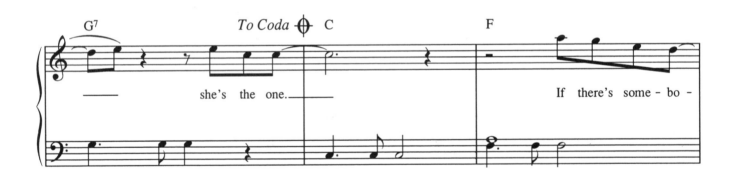

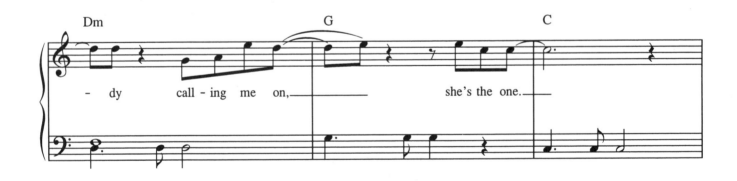

© Copyright 1996 PolyGram Music Publishing Limited.
Universal Music Publishing Limited, 77 Fulham Palace Road, London W6.
All Rights Reserved. International Copyright Secured.

1° only

F   **C**   **F**

2. We were young,___ we were wrong,___ we were fun___

C   **F**   **Dm**

___ all a - long.___ If there's some - bo — dy call - ing me on,___

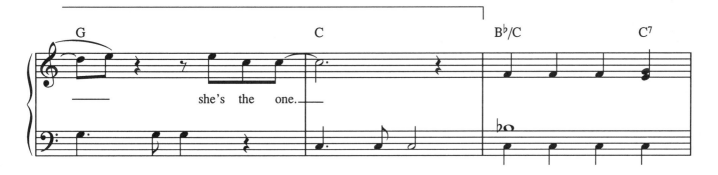

G   **C**   **B♭/C**   **C⁷**

___ she's the one.___

F

When you get to where you wan - na go, and you know the things you wan - na know,___ you're

C   **C⁷**   **F**

smil - ing.___ When you said what you wan - na say and you

know the way you wan - na play,___ yeah. You'll be so high you'll be

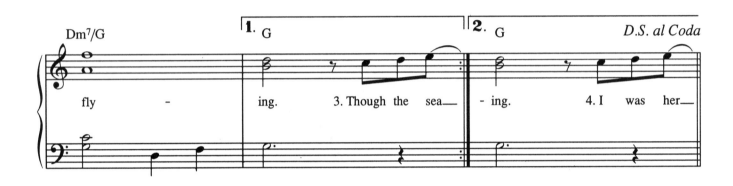

fly - ing. 3. Though the sea___ - ing. 4. I was her___

D.S. al Coda

CODA

If there's some - bo -

- dy call - ing me on,___ she's the one.___

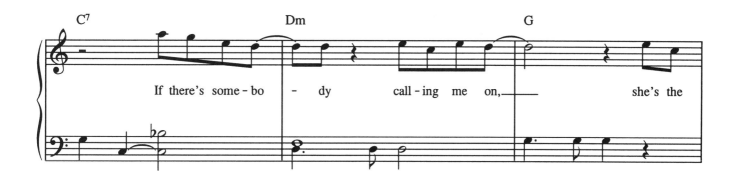

If there's some-bo - dy call-ing me on,—— she's the

one, yes, she's the one.—— If there's some-bo - dy call-ing me on,—

—— she's the one,—— she's the one.—— If there's some-bo -

- dy call-ing me on,— she's the one,——— she's the

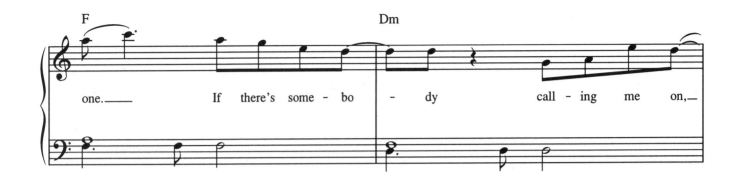

one.＿＿ If there's some - bo ＿ dy call - ing me on,＿

she's the one.＿＿

She's the one.

Verse 3:

Though the sea will be strong
I know we'll carry on
'Cos if there's somebody calling me on, she's the one
If there's somebody calling me on, she's the one.

Verse 4:

I was her, she was me
We were one, we were free
And if there's somebody calling me on *etc.*

Think Twice

Words & Music by Andy Hill & Pete Sinfield

Moderately

mf 1. Don't think I can't feel that there's some - thing wrong,____
(Verse 2 see block lyric)

you've been the sweet-est part of my life for so long. I look in your eyes, there's a

dis - tant light____ and you and I know there'll be a storm to - night.____

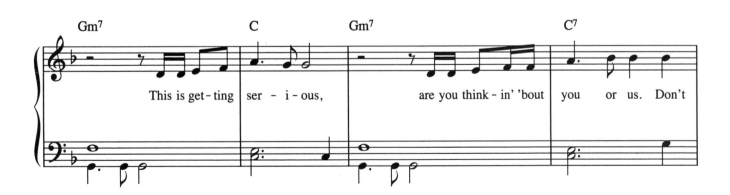

This is get-ting ser - i - ous, are you think - in' 'bout you or us. Don't

© Copyright 1993 Chrysalis Music Limited, Bramley Road, London W10 (50%)/
EMI-Virgin Music Limited, 127 Charing Cross Road, London WC2 (50%)
All Rights Reserved. International Copyright Secured.

you__ or us?__ Ba - by.__ Don't say what you're a-bout to say,__

__ look back be-fore you leave my life. Be sure be-fore you close that

Repeat to fade

door, be-fore you roll__ those__ dice. Don't

Verse 2:

Baby think twice, for the sake of our love
For the memory.
For the fire and the faith
That was you and me.
Babe I know it ain't easy
When your soul cries out for higher ground,
'Cause when you're halfway up
You're always halfway down.

But baby this is serious
Are you thinking 'bout you or us?

Un-Break My Heart

Words & Music by Dianne Warren

© Copyright 1996 Realsongs, USA.
EMI Songs Limited, 127 Charing Cross Road, London WC2.
All Rights Reserved. International Copyright Secured.

With - out you, I just can't go_____ on._____

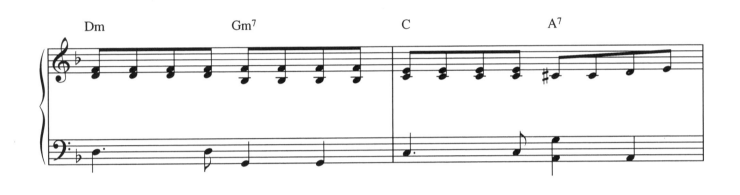

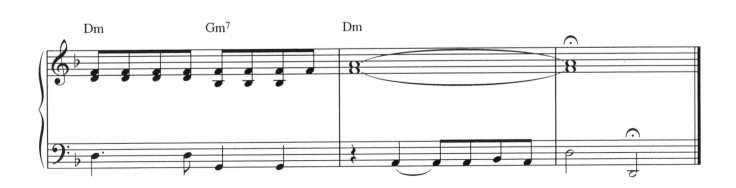

2 Become 1

Words & Music by Victoria Aadams, Melanie Brown, Emma Bunton, Melanie Chisholm, Geri Halliwell, Matt Rowe & Richard Stannard

Moderately

1. Can - dle light and soul for - ev - er a dream of you and me to -geth - er.
(Verse 2 see block lyric)

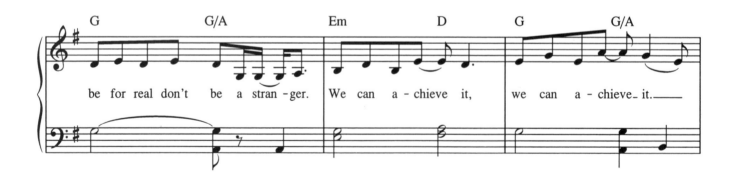

Say you be - lieve___ it, Say you be - lieve_ it, Free your mind of doubt and dan - ger,

be for real don't be a stran - ger. We can a - chieve it, we can a - chieve_ it.___

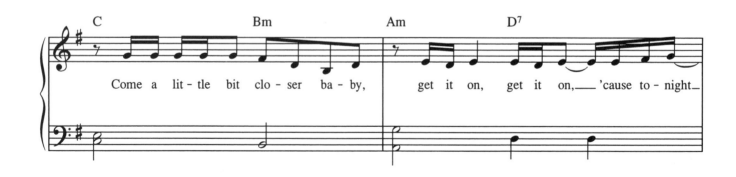

Come a lit - tle bit clo - ser ba - by, get it on, get it on,___ 'cause to - night___

© Copyright 1996 Universal Music Publishing Limited, 77 Fulham Palace Road, London W6 (50%)/
EMI Music Publishing (WP) Limited, 127 Charing Cross Road, London WC2 (50%).
All Rights Reserved. International Copyright Secured.

is the night___ when two be - come one.___ I

need some love like I ne - ver need-ed love be - fore, (wan -na make love to ya ba - by.) I

had a lit - tle love now I'm back for more, (wan -na make love to ya ba - by.)

set your spi - rit free, it's the on - ly way to be.___

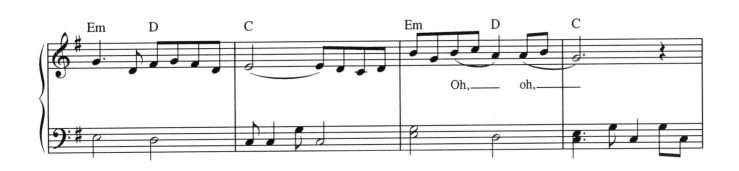

Oh,___ oh,___

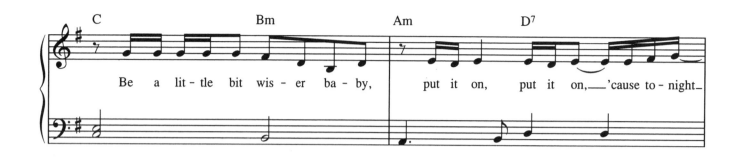

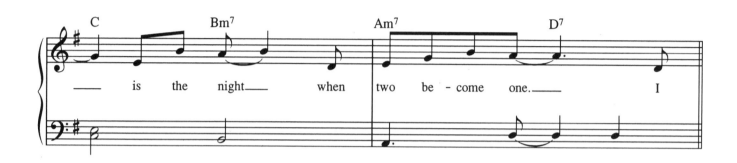

Repeat to fade

Verse 2:

Silly games that you were playing, empty words we both were saying,
Let's work it out boy, let's work it out boy.
Any deal that we endeavour, boys and girls feel good together,
Take it or leave it, take it or leave it.
Are you as good as I remember baby, get it on, get it on,
'Cause tonight is the night when two become one.

I need some love like I never needed love before, (wanna make love to ya baby.)
I had a little love, now I'm back for more, (wanna make love to ya baby.)
Set your spirit free, it's the only way to be.

When You Say Nothing At All

Words & Music by Paul Overstreet & Don Schlitz

Moderately

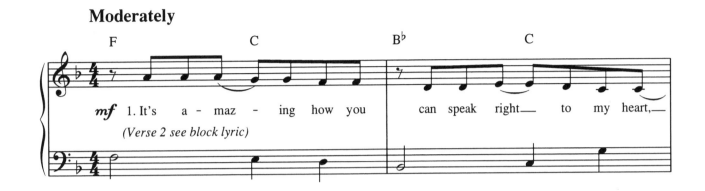

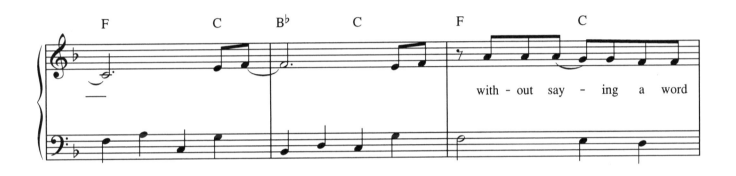

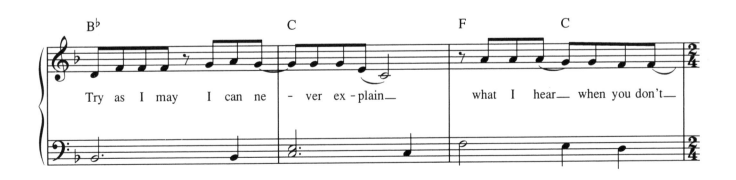

© Copyright 1993 Don Schlitz Music/Scarlet Moon Music/Screen Gems-EMI Music Incorporated, USA.
Universal/MCA Music Limited, 77 Fulham Palace Road, London W6 (50%)/BMG Music Publishing Limited, Bedford House,
69-79 Fulham High Street, London SW6 (37.5%)/Screen Gems-EMI Music Limited, 127 Charing Cross Road, London WC2 (12.5%).
This arrangement © Copyright 2001 BMG Music Publishing Limited for their share of interest.
All Rights Reserved. International Copyright Secured.

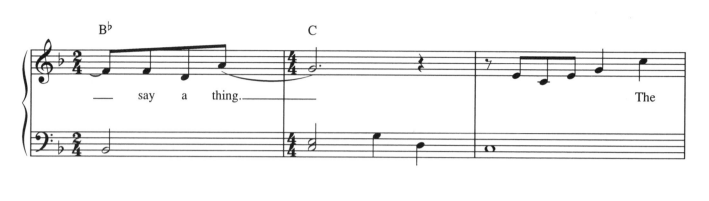

— say a thing. ___ The

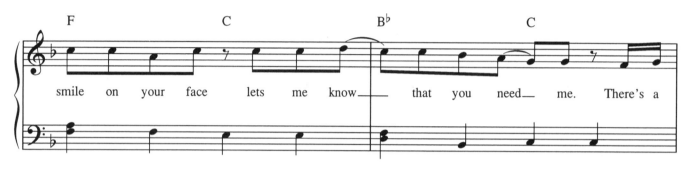

smile on your face lets me know ___ that you need ___ me. There's a

truth in your eyes say-ing you'll ___ ne-ver leave ___ me. The touch of your hand says you'll catch ___

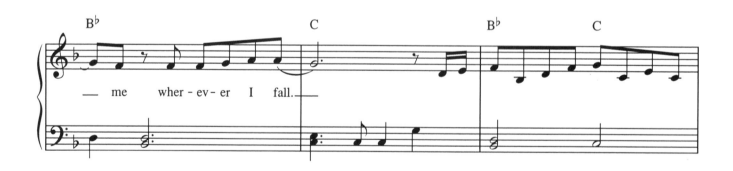

___ me wher-ev-er I fall. ___

You ___ say it best when you say no-thing at all. ___

when you say no-thing at all.

smile on your face lets me know that you need me. There's a truth in your eyes say-ing you'll ne-ver leave me. The touch of your hand says you'll catch

The

45

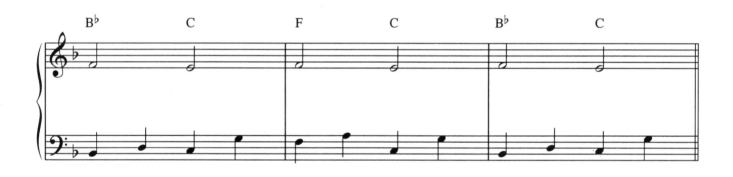

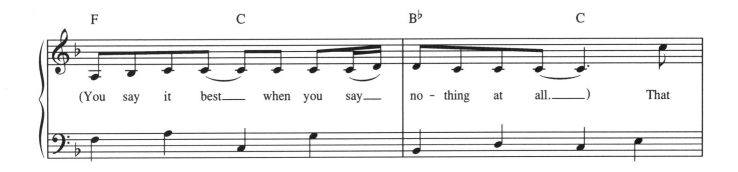

(You say it best___ when you say___ no-thing at all.____) That

smile on your face,___ there's truth in your eyes.___ The

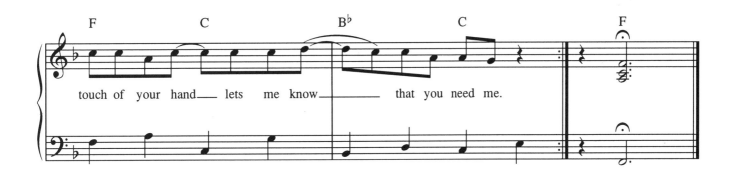

touch of your hand___ lets me know_____ that you need me.

Verse 2:

All day long I can hear people talking out loud
But when you hold me you drown out the crowd
Try as they may they can never defy
What's been said between your heart and mine.

The smile on your face *etc.*